English Language Learning

with

Super Support™

A WORKBOOK

For ESL / ESOL / EFL / ELL Students

Beginners – Book 1

CHRIS BALLI

Griselda Califa, LLC

2016

ISBN 978-0-692-76120-5

English Language - Beginner's text for foreign speakers 2. Beginning ESL/ESOL/EFL/ELL Student's Workbook 3. English Language - Basic Exercises and Activities 4. Beginning Literacy

Illustrations - author

Notes to Teachers

Objective:

The primary objective of this book is communication, which includes speaking, reading, and writing. The language structures were designed for immediate use in authentic, everyday situations. This book strives to provide the necessary language needed for these everyday situations. Most life skills, such as driving, typing, and learning a new language, for example, are learned through constant practice and repetition. The lessons in this book were therefore constructed with this in mind - with ample repetition and practice in many varied drills and exercises.

Content:

The lessons, activities, and worksheets build on each other and get more difficult in tiny, incremental steps. The beginning lessons deal with personal information that every student should know and be able to communicate. Consequently, this is the perfect material for use in class surveys, pair-reporting, and drills. Right from the start, students get a sample of the activities and written lessons that will be used throughout the book. They also get an opportunity to practice speaking immediately. They will be practicing something that is relevant and necessary and not just some random language drill.

Target Audience:

This book is for basic/beginning ESL, ESOL, EFL, and ELL students. In other words, it is for zero English speakers or minimal English speakers. Foreign students with complete educations from their own countries do not always require the entire set of exercises provided. Lessons can be selected to target specific trouble spots or for additional practice and reinforcement.

Students from war-torn countries, illiterate students, or students with gaps in their educations benefit from doing the entire set of exercises in this book. This material has been very effective in helping these groups.

What You Can Expect:

You can expect students to start speaking sooner than usual. You can expect vocabulary development for an improvement in reading. You can also expect students to advance quickly in writing independently.

This book works!

Table of Contents

Table of Contents

Lesson #1

Information about Myself

Greetings and Introductions

Good Morning

A. Good morning. How are you?
B. Fine, thank you, and you?
A. Fine, thank you.

Introducing Myself

A. Hi. My name is Mary.
   What is your name?
B. My name is Sue.
A. Nice to meet you, Sue. (shake hands)
B. It's nice to meet you, too.

Activity: Each student will get up and introduce themselves to at least 5 people in the class.

Introducing Someone Else

You: Hi, Mary. I'd like to introduce you to Sally.
Mary: It's a pleasure to meet you, Sally.
Sally: It's a pleasure to meet you, too, Mary.

Story about Mary Garza

My name is Mary Garza.
I am 16 years old.
I speak Spanish.
I am from Mexico.
I live in Beeville, California.
My address is:

Mary Garza
300 Main Street
Apt. # 25
Beeville, California 54321

My phone number is (123) 555-0199.
I go to Blake High School.
I am in the 10th grade.
I ride bus #31 to school.
There are seven people in my family.
I work at Betty's Burger Barn after school.
My date of birth is October 20, 1999.

Questions about Mary Garza

1. What is your name?

   My name is_____.

2. How old are you?

   I am_____.

3. What language do you speak?

   I speak_____.

4. Where are you from?

   I am from_____.

5. Where do you live?

   I live in_____.

6. What is your address?
   My address is

   _____

   _____

   _____

7.   What is your phone number?

    My phone number is _____.

8.   What school do you go to?

    I go to _____.

9.   What grade are you in?

    I am in the _____grade.

10. What bus do you ride to school?

    I ride bus number #_____ to school.   (or)

    I don't ride the bus.

11. How many people are in your family?

    There are _____ people in my family.

12. Where do you work?
    I work at _____.

13. What is your date of birth?
    My date of birth is _____.

A Story about Me

[(your picture)]

My name is _____.

I am _____ years old.

I speak _____.

I am from_____.

I live in _____.

My address is:

_____

_____

_____

My phone number is _____.

I go to _____school.

I am in the_____ grade.

I ride bus #_____ to school.   (or)   I don't ride the bus.

There are _____ people in my family.

I work at_____.   (or)   I don't work.

My date of birth is _____.

Questions about Me

Answer in complete sentences.

1. What is your name?

   _____

2. Where are you from?

   _____

3. What language do you speak?

   _____

4. Where do you live?

   _____

5. What is your phone number?

   _____

6. How old are you?

   _____

7. What is your date of birth?

_____

8. How many people are in your family?

_____

9. Where do you go to school?

_____

10. What grade are you in?

_____

11. Where do you work?

_____

12. What is your address:

_____

_____

_____

_____

Let's Talk!
Two Speaking Activities

#1: Class Survey

*Walk around the room and **talk to** __5__ **classmates.** Ask them these **3** questions.*

* Your classmates should **answer in a complete sentence.**

1. **What is your name?**   My name is _____ .
2. **Where are you from?**   I am from _____ .
3. **What language do you speak?**   I speak _____ .

#2: Partner Work

*Answer these questions **about yourself** and **write the answers.***

*Choose a partner and **take turns asking** each other these questions. Remember to answer in complete sentences, just like what is on this paper.*

1. **What is your name?**   My name is _____ .

2. **Where are you from?**   I am from _____ .

3. **What language do you speak?**   I speak _____ .

4. **Where do you live?**   I live in _____ .

5. **What is your phone number?**   My phone number is _____ .

6. **What grade are you in?**   I am in the ___ grade.   (or)   I don't go to school.

7. **Where do you work?**   I work at _____ .   (or)   I don't work.

8. **What is your address?**   My address is _____ .

Lesson #2

Learning to Answer Questions
about
Someone Else

Tuan Nguyen

Read the story.

My name is Tuan Nguyen.
I am 28 years old.
I speak Vietnamese.
I am from Vietnam.
I live in Sunnytown, Texas.

My address is:

    Tuan Nguyen
    456 Pelican Street
    Sunnytown, Texas 90909

My phone number is (191) 555-0100.
I don't go to school.
I work.
I work at Elmer's Electronics.
I ride bus # 65 to work.
There are 3 people in my family.
They are my wife, my son, and me.
My date of birth is May 11, 1988.

Answering Questions About
Tuan Nguyen

A. Miss Jones, can you please **answer some questions about your friend?**

B. Yes.

A. What is his name?

B. His name is _____ Tuan Nguyen _____ .

A. How old is he?

B. He is _____ years old.

A. What language does he speak?

B. He speaks_____.

A. Where is he from?

B. He is from_____.

A. What is his address?

B. His address is _____

_____

_____

A. What is his phone number?

B. His phone number is _____.

A. What grade is he in?

B. He doesn't go to school.

A. Where does he work?

B. He works at _____.

A. What bus does he ride to work?

B. He rides bus _____.

A. How many people are in his family?

B. There are _____ people in his family.

A. Who are they?

B. They are his_____, his_____, and him.

A. What is his date of birth?

B. His date of birth is_____.

Let's Talk about Dad

Story about My Father
(or any male relative)

Fill in the blanks with information about your father or male relative:

This is a story about my _____.
His name is _____.
He is from _____.
He speaks _____.
He works at _____.
(or)
He goes to school at _____.
He is _____ years old.

Speaking Practice with Partner – Using "he" in oral response

*Choose a partner. **You and your partner will take turns asking** *each other these questions.* **Answer in complete sentences.** *You and your partner* **will just listen** *to the answers.*

(**Do not write any answers.** *These questions are* **just for speaking** *and* **listening** *to each other.*)

Q: Tell me about your relative. Is this story about your father, brother, uncle, or son?
A: The story is about my _____.

Q: What is his name?
A: His name is _____.

Q: What language does he speak?
A: He speaks _____.

Q: Where is he from?
A: He is from _____.

Q: Where does he work?   (or)   Where does he go to school?
A: He works at _____.   (or)   He goes to school at _____.

Let's Talk about Mom

Story about My Mother
(or any female relative)

Fill in the blanks with information about your mother or female relative:

This is a story about my   _____.
Her name is   _____.
She is from   _____.
She speaks   _____.
She goes to school at   _____.
(or)
She works at   _____.

Speaking Practice with Partner – Using "she" in oral response

Choose a partner. You and your partner will take turns asking these questions. Answer in complete sentences. You and your partner will just listen to the answers.

(Do not write any answers. These questions are just for speaking and listening.)

Q: Tell me about your relative. Is this story about your mother, grandmother, aunt, sister, or daughter?
A: The story is about my   _____.

Q: What is her name?
A: Her name is   _____.

Q: Where is she from?
A: She is from   _____.

Q: What language does she speak?
A: She speaks   _____.

Q: Where does she work?   (or)   Where does she go to school?
A: She works at _____.   She goes to school at_____.

Writing and Reporting –
What Your Partner Tells You

(1) **Writing** What My Partner Tells Me

*Choose a partner and ask your partner to tell you the story about Mom or Dad. Then **ask** these questions and **write** your partner's answers. Next, your partner will ask you the questions and write your answers.*

(*Write what your partner answers.)*

Q: Who is the story about?
Partner's Answer: The story is about my _____.

Q: What is his/her name?
Partner's Answer: His/Her name is _____.

Q: Where is he/she from?
Partner's Answer: He/She is from _____.

Q: What language does he/she speak?
Partner's Answer: He/She speaks _____.

Q: Where does he/she work or go to school?
Partner's Answer: He/She works at _____.

(or)

He/She goes to school at _____.

---

*Use this information to fill out the **report form** on the **next page**.*

(2) **Reporting** My Partner's Story

Example: ***This is how I will report my partner's story.***

Hi. My name is <u>Mary.</u>
I interviewed <u>Sandra.</u>
This is what I know about <u>Sandra's</u> relative.
The story is about her <u>father.</u>
His name is <u>Jose.</u>
He speaks <u>Spanish.</u>
He is from <u>El Salvador.</u>
He works at <u>Don's Lawn Service.</u>
This is what I know about <u>Sandra's father.</u>

Mary   Sandra

Report Form

Fill out this report form with the information your partner gave you. *You and your partner will go in front of the class.*
*You will report on your partner's story. Then your **partner will report on your story.***

Hi. My name is _____.
                              (your name)
I interviewed _____.
                              (partner's name)
This is what I know about _____'s   relative.
                              (partner's name)

The story is about his/her _____.
His/Her name is _____.
He/She speaks _____.
He/She is from _____.
He/She works at _____ or
He/She goes to school at _____.
This is what I know about _____ _____.
                              (partner's name)   (partner's relative)

*Tomorrow, **bring a picture of a relative or friend** that you want to write a story about and report on.*

Reporting My Story

Fill out this report.
Go to the front of the class and show the picture of your friend or relative.
Tell your story to the class.

(Write your name on the first line. Then write the information about the person in your picture.)

Reporting My Story

Hi. My name is_____.

This is a picture of my _____.

His/Her name is _____.

He/She is from _____.

He/She speaks _____.

He/She goes to school at _____.

He/She works at _____.

I like to spend time with _____.
                              (name of person in the picture)
because he/she   * * *   _____.

* * * (possible things to write)

is fun to be with	helps me	is nice to me
makes me laugh	takes me places	understands me
is very interesting	talks to me	listens to me
makes me feel good	teaches me many things	
likes the same things I do		

Lesson #3

Home and Neighborhood

The Home

kitchen

Mrs. Keen (she)

dining room

Meg (she)

living room

Grandfather and Grandmother (they)

bedroom	the twins (they)
bathroom	the dog (it)
basement	Bob (he)
garage	Mr. Keen (he)
yard	the cat (it)

Saturday Morning

It is Saturday morning. Everybody in the family is in different parts of the house. This is where they are.

1. **Mr. Keen** is in the garage.
2. **Mrs. Keen** is in the kitchen.
3. **The twins** are in the bedroom.
4. **Meg** is in the dining room.
5. **The dog** is in the bathroom.
6. **Bob** is in the basement.
7. **The cat** is in the yard.
8. **Grandfather and Grandmother** are in the living room.

(a)   *Rewrite the sentences using the subject pronouns —* **He   She   It   They**
      Look at the pictures to see which pronoun to use.

  1. **Mr. Keen** is in the garage.
      He _____ is in the garage.

  2. _____.

      _____.

  3. _____.

      _____.

  4. _____.

      _____.

  5. _____.

      _____.

3-2: continued

6. _____ .

_____ .

7. _____ .

_____ .

8. _____ .

_____ .

9. _____ .

_____ .

*Partner Work: Get a partner. You read the sentence. Your partner reads the sentence **with the pronoun.**

Example:
You: "Mr. Keen is in the garage."
Partner: "He is in the garage."

(b) Vocabulary Expansion:

Have students find **pictures of furniture** commonly found in the rooms of a house. Each student will choose a room and make a poster of the furniture found in that room. Students will **label the furniture.** Students will present their posters to the class. The posters will be hung around the room.

(**Items** can also be included, such as dishes for the kitchen, pillows for the bedroom, etc.)

Write Your Own Sentences

Where are you?

*(a)*Write 10 sentences using this chart. Take 1 line from each column to form a
  sentence. You can use the lines in any order.*

I am You are He is She is It is We are They are Grandmother and Grandfather are Bob is Meg is The dog is	in the	kitchen. living room. dining room. bathroom. bedroom. basement. garage. yard.

Example: *I am in the kitchen.*
            You are in the basement.

1._____.

2._____.

3._____.

4._____.

5._____.

6._____.

7._____.

8._____.

9._____.

10._____.

What are you **doing?**

(b) Write 15 sentences using this chart. Take 1 line from each column to form a sentence.
You can use the lines in any order.*

I am	sleeping.
You are	cleaning.
He is	cooking.
She is	making breakfast/lunch/dinner.
It is	eating breakfast/lunch/dinner.
We are	drinking coffee.
They are	reading the paper.
Mr. Keen is	watching TV.
Mrs. Keen is	taking a shower.
Meg is	getting dressed.
Bob is	washing the car.
The twins are	washing dishes.
Grandmother is	vacuuming.
Grandfather is	doing the laundry.
My mother is	folding the clothes.
My father is	putting away the clothes.
My brother is	picking up toys.
My sister is	sweeping.
The dog is	mopping.
The cat is	taking out the trash.
	raking the yard.
	mowing the lawn.
	drinking water.
	chasing a bird.

*Example: I am making breakfast.
You are drinking coffee.*

1. I am sleeping _____ .

2. _____ .

Example: *She is making breakfast.*
I am eating lunch.

3.＿＿＿＿＿＿＿＿＿＿＿＿＿＿＿＿＿＿＿＿＿＿＿＿＿＿.

4.＿＿＿＿＿＿＿＿＿＿＿＿＿＿＿＿＿＿＿＿＿＿＿＿＿＿.

5.＿＿＿＿＿＿＿＿＿＿＿＿＿＿＿＿＿＿＿＿＿＿＿＿＿＿.

6.＿＿＿＿＿＿＿＿＿＿＿＿＿＿＿＿＿＿＿＿＿＿＿＿＿＿.

7.＿＿＿＿＿＿＿＿＿＿＿＿＿＿＿＿＿＿＿＿＿＿＿＿＿＿.

8.＿＿＿＿＿＿＿＿＿＿＿＿＿＿＿＿＿＿＿＿＿＿＿＿＿＿.

9.＿＿＿＿＿＿＿＿＿＿＿＿＿＿＿＿＿＿＿＿＿＿＿＿＿＿.

10.＿＿＿＿＿＿＿＿＿＿＿＿＿＿＿＿＿＿＿＿＿＿＿＿＿.

11.＿＿＿＿＿＿＿＿＿＿＿＿＿＿＿＿＿＿＿＿＿＿＿＿＿.

12.＿＿＿＿＿＿＿＿＿＿＿＿＿＿＿＿＿＿＿＿＿＿＿＿＿.

13.＿＿＿＿＿＿＿＿＿＿＿＿＿＿＿＿＿＿＿＿＿＿＿＿＿.

14.＿＿＿＿＿＿＿＿＿＿＿＿＿＿＿＿＿＿＿＿＿＿＿＿＿.

15.＿＿＿＿＿＿＿＿＿＿＿＿＿＿＿＿＿＿＿＿＿＿＿＿＿.

16.＿＿＿＿＿＿＿＿＿＿＿＿＿＿＿＿＿＿＿＿＿＿＿＿＿.

Speaking:

Get a partner and take turns reading the sentences you wrote for
"Where are you?" and "What are you doing?"

Putting it all together:
Where are they and what are they doing?

3-3: (c)
Read the sentences and think about where they are. Look in the box to find the answers. Write the correct answer on the lines.

What are they doing?	Where are they?
1. Dad is cleaning the car.	*He is in the garage* _____.
2. Grandfather is taking a shower.	_____.
3. Bob is mowing the lawn.	_____.

Answer Box
He is in the yard.
~~He is in the garage.~~
He is in the bathroom.

4. The twins are sleeping.	_____.
5. Meg and Bob are doing the laundry.	_____.
6. Grandfather and Grandmother are drinking coffee.	_____.

Answer Box
They are in the dining room.
They are in the basement.
They are in the bedroom.

Putting it all together:
Where are they and what are they doing?

What are they doing?	Where are they?
7. Mrs. Keen is cooking.	_____.
8. Grandmother is watching TV.	_____.
9. Meg is raking the leaves.	_____.

Answer Box
She is in the living room.
She is in the kitchen.
She is in the yard.

Get a partner. You read "What are they doing?" Your partner reads "Where are they?"

Saturday Afternoon in

The Neighborhood

Now it is Saturday afternoon. Everybody in the family is in different places in the neighborhood. Write a sentence to tell us where they are. Write another sentence to tell us what they are doing.

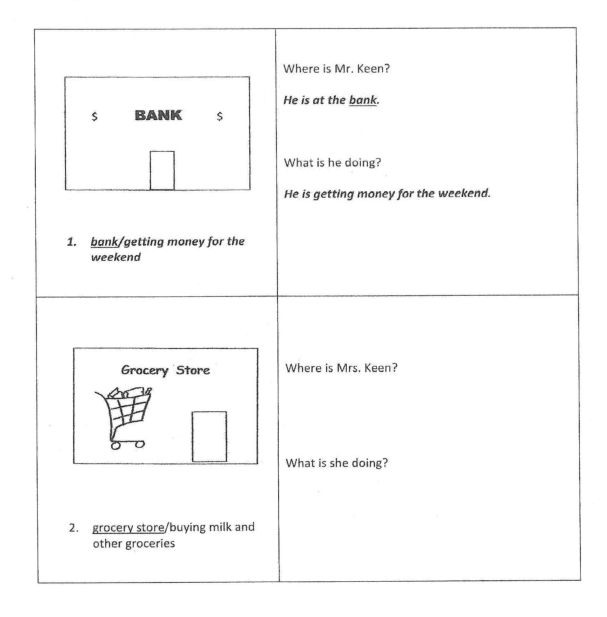

Where is Mr. Keen?

He is at the <u>bank</u>.

What is he doing?

He is getting money for the weekend.

1. <u>bank</u>/getting money for the weekend

Where is Mrs. Keen?

What is she doing?

2. <u>grocery store</u>/buying milk and other groceries

3-4: continued

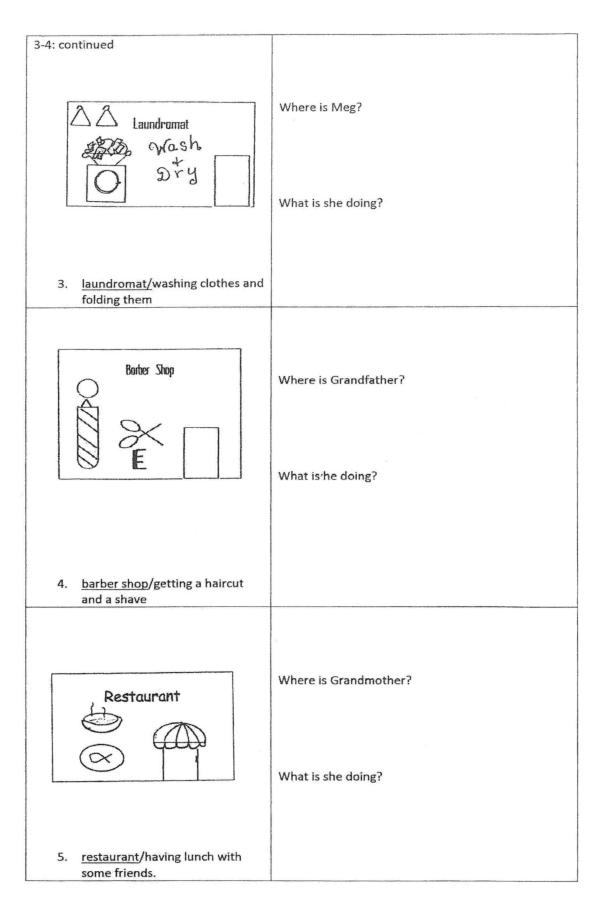

Where is Meg?

What is she doing?

3. laundromat/washing clothes and folding them

Where is Grandfather?

What is he doing?

4. barber shop/getting a haircut and a shave

Where is Grandmother?

What is she doing?

5. restaurant/having lunch with some friends.

3-4: continued

City Park	Where are the twins?
6. park/playing with their cousins.	What are they doing?
Hardware Store	Where is Bob?
7. hardware store/buying a rake	What is he doing?
City Park	Where is the dog?
8. park/playing with the twins	What is it doing?

*Get a partner. You ask the questions. Your partner answers the questions. Take turns asking and answering.

What about you?

(Applying What You've Learned)

* **It is Saturday. Where are you? Where is your family? What are you and your family doing?**

* *Write as many sentences as you can telling where you and your family are, and what you are doing.*

_____

_____

_____

_____

_____

_____

_____

_____

_____

_____

_____

_____

*Get a partner. Read your sentences to your partner. Next, listen to your partner's sentences.

Write Sentences
About the Neighborhood

*Use this chart to write **17 sentences about places in the neighborhood**.*

I am You are He is She is It is We are They are Dad is Mom is My grandparents are Mr. Keen is Mrs. Keen is Bob is Meg is The twins are My friends are My friend and I are	at the	bank. grocery store. movies. bakery. restaurant. laundromat. library. florist. barbershop. beauty shop. hardware store. doctor's office. pharmacy. drugstore. gas station. park.

Example:
I am at the grocery store.
You are at the doctor's office.

1. _____*I am at the bank*_____.

2. _____.

3. _____.

4. _____.

5. _____.

17 Sentences about Places in the Neighborhood (continued)

6. _____.

7. _____.

8. _____.

9. _____.

10. _____.

11. _____.

12. _____.

13. _____.

14. _____.

15. _____.

16. _____.

17. _____.

18. _____.

Get a partner. Read your 17 sentences to each other.

Quiz
Subject Pronouns and Subject Verb Agreement

*(1) Rewrite the sentences using - **He, She, They, It.***

    1. <u>Mrs. Keen</u> is in the living room.
       She *is in the living room.*

    2. Mr. Keen is in the basement.

    3. Meg is in the kitchen.

    4. The twins are in the garage.

    5. The dog is in the yard.

    6. Grandfather and Grandmother are in the dining room.

    7. Bob is in the bedroom.

    8. The cat is in the bathroom.

(2) Write sentences with these words.
    (*Remember - I am, You are, He is, She is, It is, We are, They are.)

    1. They — park.
       They are at the park.

    2. She — library.

    3. You — gas station.

    4. They — laundromat.

    5. You — barber shop.

    6. She — beauty shop.

    7. We — grocery store.

Quiz (continued)

8. My Grandparents — bakery.

9. Mr. Keen - bank.

10. Mrs. Keen — pharmacy.

11. Bob — hardware store.

12. Meg — florist.

13. The dog — the dog park.

14. The twins — movies.

*(3) Fill in the blanks with – **am, are, is**.*

1. I _____ eating.
   I ___**am**___ eating.

2. You _____drinking coffee.
   You ___**are**___ drinking coffee.

3. She _____drinking tea.
   She ___**is**___ drinking tea.

4. I _____cleaning my room.

5. You _____sweeping.

6. He _____vacuuming.

7. She _____mopping.

8. It _____sleeping.

9. We _____putting away our clothes.

10. They _____picking up their toys.

Quiz (continued)

*(Fill in the blanks with – **am, are, is**.)*

11. Mr. Keen _____ mowing the lawn.

12. Mrs. Keen _____ making lunch.

13. Grandfather and Grandmother _____ reading the newspaper.

14. Bob _____ raking the yard.

15. The dog _____ drinking water.

16. Meg _____ doing the laundry.

17. The twins _____ getting dressed.

18. The cat _____ chasing a bird.

19. I _____ watching TV.

20. He _____ taking out the trash.

Lesson #4

Places in the School

Lesson #4

Places in the School

Art Class
Auditorium
Cafeteria/Lunch Room
Computer Class
Counselor's Office
English Class
ESOL Class
Gym
History Class
Library/Media Center

Locker
Main Office
Math Class
Music Class
Nurse/Health Room
PE Locker Rooms
PE/Physical Education
Reading Class
Restrooms
Science Class

Present Continuous

I am going to math class.

You are going to math class.

He is going to math class.

She is going to math class.

It is going to math class.

We are going to math class.

You (plural) are going to math class.

They are going to math class.

Places in the School: Names

1. History Class	2. Math Class	3. Art Class	4. English Class
5. ESOL Class	6. Science Class	7. Music Class	8. Reading Class
9. PE /Physical Education	10. Gym-gymnasium	11. PE Locker Rooms	12. Nurse/Health Room
13. Library/Media Center	14. Computer Class	15. Main Office	16. Cafeteria/Lunch Room
17. Counselor's Office	18. Restrooms	19. Locker	20. Auditorium

Label the Places in the School

1.	2.	3.	4.
5.	6.	7.	8.
9.	10.	11.	12.
13.	14.	15.	16.

Word Bank

Art Class		Music Class
Auditorium	Gym/gymnasium	Nurse/Health Room
Cafeteria/Lunch Room	History Class	PE
Computer Class	Library/Media Center	PE Locker Rooms
Counselor's Office	Lockers	Reading Class
English Class	Main Office	Restrooms
ESOL Class	Math Class	Science Class

Where are you going?

*Write sentences using this chart. Write 3 sentences for each pronoun.
(Choose any line from the last column to finish your sentences.)

*The teacher will call on different students to read one of their sentences.

I am You are He is She is We are They are	going	to	PE class math class science class reading class ESOL class English class history class art class the cafeteria the gym the library the music room the main office the counselor's office the nurse the girls' locker room the restroom the water fountain the lockers

Example: I am going to <u>the cafeteria.</u>
I am going to <u>English class.</u>

1. I am going to _____ *PE class* _____ .
2. I am going to _____ *the water fountain* _____ .
3. I am going *to* _____ *English class* _____ .

4. You are going to_____ .

5. You are going to_____ .

6. You are going to_____ .

Where are you going?

7. He is going to_____.

8. He is going to_____.

9. He is going to_____.

10. She is going to_____.

11. She is going to_____.

12. She is going to_____.

13. We are going to_____.

14. We are going to_____.

15. We are going to_____.

16. They are going to_____.

17. They are going to_____.

18. They are going to_____.

19. I am going to_____.

20. I am going to_____.

21. I am going to_____.

4-5:   (Good for first week of school.)

Drama/Role Playing/Activity
"Where are you going?"

Activity #1: Where are **you** going?

Teacher: Where are **you** going?
Student: I am going to _____.
                    (the gym, the cafeteria, PE, etc.)

- The teacher calls on a student to go to the door and to pretend he or she is going out the door.
- The teacher asks, "Where are you going?"
- The student answers, " I am going to_____ .

- The teacher practices the role playing with several more students.

Next, students will take turns being the teacher and asking, "Where are you going?"
Several students will take turns going out the door.

Activity #2: Where is **he** going?

Mary: Joe, where are you going?

Jòe: I am going _____ .

Teacher: Where is **he** going?

Class: **He** is going _____ .

Activity #3: Where is **she** going?

Joe: Mary, where are you going?

Mary: I am going_____ .

Teacher: Where is **she** going?

Class: **She** is going_____ .

Activity #4: Where are **they** going?

Teacher: Mary and Joe, where are you going? Mary and Joe: We are going _____.	Teacher: Where are **they** going? Class: **They** are going_____.

Students take turns being Mary, Joe, and the Teacher for all of the activities.

Subject Pronouns:
Review

Fill in the correct pronoun and verb: **He is**
                                       She is
                                       They are

	1. **He** **is** going to the cafeteria.
	2. ____ _____ going to the cafeteria.
	3. ____ _____ going to the cafeteria.

Writing Your Own Sentences:
Tell Where They Are Going

*Look at the pictures. Think about where they are going. Write sentences that tell where they are going. Decide if you should start the sentence with **"He is, She is, or They Are."***

	1. *They are going to science class.*
	2.
	3.

Word Box		
art class	the cafeteria	history class
music class	PE	science class

	4.
	5.
	6.

Word Box

art class	the cafeteria	history class
music class	PE	science class

Answering the Question

Example:

    * Where are **you** going? (the gym)
      I am going to the gym.

    * Where is **he** going?   (the gym)
      He is going to the gym.

    * Where is **she** going? (the gym)
      She is going to the gym.

    * Where are **they** going? (the gym)
      They are going to the gym.

*Write the answers in **complete sentences**.*

1. Where are you going?   (the cafeteria)

2. Where is he going?   (the restroom)

3. Where is she going?   (the water fountain)

4. Where are they going?   (PE)

5. Where is he going?   (room 157)

6. Where are you going?   (science class)

7. Where is she going?   (the nurse's office)

8. Where is he going?   (the gym)

9. Where are they going?   (the library)

Telling the Location

Example:

I am in the cafeteria.
You are in the cafeteria.
She is in the cafeteria.
He is in the cafeteria.
It is in the cafeteria.
We are in the cafeteria.
You (plural) **are** in the cafeteria.
They are in the cafeteria.

Where is **Mrs. Jones?**   *She is in the cafeteria.*

Where is **Mr. Smith?**   *He is in the office.*

Where are **Sam and Bob?**   *They are in math class.*

Writing: Write 20 Sentences Using This Chart:

I am You are He is Mr. Smith is She is Mrs. Brown is It is We are They are Bob and Mary are	in PE class. in the gym. in science class. in English class. in ESOL class. in history class. in the art room. in the library. in the restroom. in the main office. at the water fountain. at the lockers.

1. _I am in PE class_ .

2. _Mr. Smith is in the main office_ .

3. _____ .

Telling the Location

4. _____.

5. _____.

6. _____.

7. _____.

8. _____.

9. _____.

10. _____.

11. _____.

12. _____.

13. _____.

14. _____.

15. _____.

16. _____.

17. _____.

18. _____.

19. _____.

20. _____.

21. _____.

22. _____.

The teacher will call on students to read some of their sentences.

Speaking Practice:

Questions for
Automatic Response

The teacher will write these questions on the board and call on different students to answer.
* The student can say any location but must answer with a complete sentence.*
The objective is to try to answer automatically.

1. Where are you?
2. Where is Mrs. Jones?
3. Where is the Principal?
4. Where is Bob?
5. Where is Mary?
6. Where are Mary and Bob?
7. Where is Miss Moon?
8. Where am I?
9. Where is the counselor?
10. Where is your teacher?
11. Where is the nurse?
12. Where is the coach?
13. Where is the art teacher?
14. Where is the English teacher?

Partner Work:

Choose a partner.
Take turns asking each other the questions.
Try to answer automatically. You can answer any location.

Questions: Trying to Find People

Write 9 questions using this chart.

Grammar Help: * *Where **is she**?*   *Where **is he**?*   *Where **are they**?*
                             *Where **are you**?*

Excuse me,	where	* is are	Mrs. Jones? Mr. Jones? Mr. and Mrs. Smith? Bob? Mary? Mr. Sands? Bob and Mary? you? my mother? my friends? my sister? Mrs. Jones?

1. _____ *Excuse me, where is Mrs. Jones* _____ ?

2. _____ *Excuse me, where are my friends* _____ ?

3. _____

4. _____

5. _____

6. _____

7. _____

8. _____

9. _____

10. _____

11. _____

What is the Question?

*Look in the *box* and **find the question** that goes with the answer.

Where is Mr. Jones?	1. **He** is in the cafeteria.
	2. **She** is in the main office.
	3. **They** are in the library.
	4. **I** am in the science lab.
	5. **He** is in room 157.

- ~~*Where is Mr. Jones?*~~
- *Where is **Mr. Smith**?*
- *Where are **you**?*
- *Where is my **sister**?*
- *Where are **Bob and Bill**?*

	6. **They** are in the gym.
	7. **He** is in computer class.
	8. **She** is in the nurse's office.
	9. **I** am in English class.

- *Where are **you**?*
- *Where is **Mary**?*
- *Where are my **friends**?*
- *Where is **Bob**?*

Answering in Complete Sentences

*Read the question then *write the answer in a complete sentence.*
*Grammar Help: **He is   She is   They are   I am**

1. Where are <u>you</u>? (in ESOL class)

   *I **am** in ESOL class.*

2. Where is **Mrs. Green**? (in her classroom)

3. Where is **Mr. Turner**? (in the science lab)

4. Where are **you**? (in math class)

5. Where is **Tom?** (in the computer lab)

6. Where is **Mary?** (in the counselor's office)

7. Where is **Mrs. Smith**? (in the main office)

8. Where is **Mrs. Wong?** (in the library)

9. Where are **Sue and Sam?** (in the cafeteria)

10. Where are **you?** (?)

Questions: Trying to Find Places

Write 6 questions using this chart.

Excuse me,	where is	room 157? the gym? the bathroom? the library? the science room? the cafeteria? the art room? the water fountain?

Partner Work: Speaking Practice

Your teacher will ask students to read their questions.
 Next, she will explain some answers that you might hear if you ask someone these questions.

Choose a partner.
Take turns asking each other the questions and giving the possible answers.

Possible Answers:

1. Go straight. Turn right. /Go straight. Turn left.
2. It is around the corner.
3. It is at the end of the hall, on the left. /It is at the end of the hall, on the right.
4. It is upstairs.
5. It is downstairs.
6. It is across from the cafeteria.
7. It is next to the gym.
8. It is on the third floor.
9. I don't know.

Quiz

(1) *Fill in the sentences with the correct verb — **am, are, is.***

1. I _____*am*_____ going to the cafeteria.
2. You _____*are*_____ going to the library.
3. He _____*is*_____ going to the main office.
4. She _____ going to history class.
5. We _____ going to math class.
6. They _____ going to English class.
7. He _____ going to science class.
8. Bob _____ going to music class.
9. She _____ going to art class.
10. Meg _____ going to reading class.
11. They _____ going to PE.
12. The twins _____ going to the gym.
13. We _____ going to the auditorium.
14. You _____ going to computer class.
15. He _____ going to the PE locker room.
16. Mr. Keen _____ going to the main office.
17. Mrs. Keen _____ going to the counselor's office.
18. My friends _____ going to the cafeteria.
19. My teacher, Mr. Brown, _____ going to the library.
20. She _____ going to the health room.
21. We _____ going to the gym.
22. He _____ going to the restroom.
23. They _____ going to ESOL class.

(2) *Answer the questions.*
*Remember - **I am, You are, She is, He is, It is, We are, They are.***

1. Where are you? (in the gym)
    I am in the gym.

2. Where is she?   (in the art room)

3. Where are they?   (in the cafeteria)

Quiz (continued)

4. Where is he?   (in PE class)

5. Where is she?   (in art class)

6. Where are they?   (in the gym)

7. Where are we?   (in English class)

8. Where is Bob?   (at his locker)

9. Where are Bob and Meg?   (in the auditorium)

10. Where is Mr. Brown?   (outside)

11. Where is Mrs. Smith?   (upstairs)

12. Where is Meg?   (at the water fountain)

13. Where is Mr. Gray?   (in his classroom)

14. Where are you?   (in computer class)

15. Where is he?   (in the restroom)

16. Where is Mary?   (in the health room)

Quiz (continued)

17. Where are we?   (in the library)

18. Where is Mr. Brown, our principal?   (main office)

19. Where is Mrs. Wells, my teacher?   (in her classroom)

(3) *Write 7 questions.*

1. (Where - Mr. Smith)

   Where is Mr. Smith?

2. (Where - Bob)

3. (Where – Mary)

4. (Where – my friends)

5. (Where – my teacher)

6. (Where – Bob and Mary)

7. (Where – they)

8. (Where – it)

Lesson #5

School Vocabulary

School Vocabulary

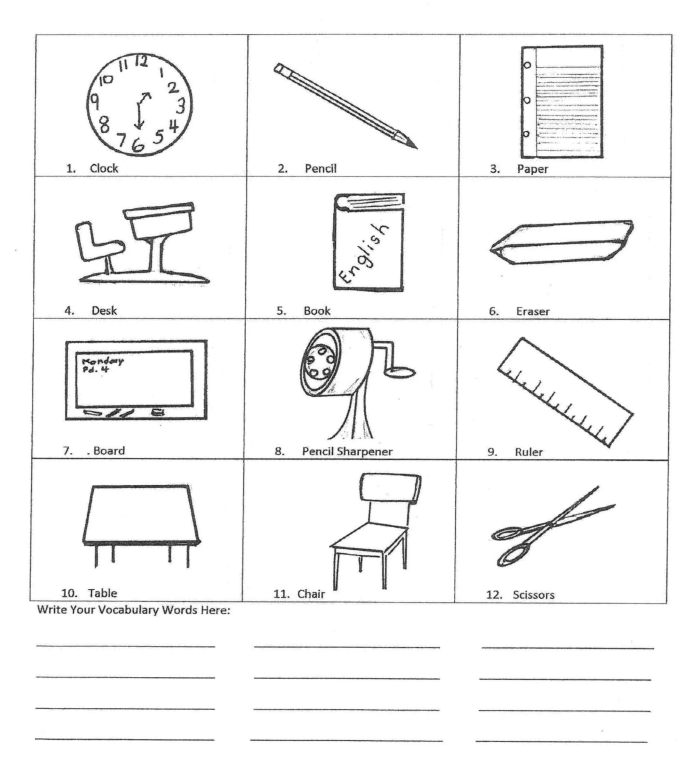

1. Clock
2. Pencil
3. Paper
4. Desk
5. Book
6. Eraser
7. . Board
8. Pencil Sharpener
9. Ruler
10. Table
11. Chair
12. Scissors

Write Your Vocabulary Words Here:

_____   _____   _____

_____   _____   _____

_____   _____   _____

_____   _____   _____

13. Pen	14. Spiral Notebook	15. Calculator
16. Glue	17. Stapler	18. Tape
19. Backpack	20. Crayons	21. Paper Clip
22. Marker	23. Paint Brush	24. Paint

Write the Vocabulary Words

_____   _____   _____

_____   _____   _____

_____   _____   _____

_____   _____   _____

Label the Pictures: School Vocabulary

*Write the correct word under the pictures.

WORD BOX: Crayons Pencil Pen	1.	2.	3.
Eraser Ruler Paper	4.	5.	6.
Book Glue Scissors	7.	8.	9.
Marker Paint brush Paint	10.	11.	12.

Paper Clip Board Clock	Monday Pd. 4 13.	14.	15.
Stapler Calculator Desk	16.	17.	18.
Tape Pencil Sharpener Spiral Notebook	19.	20.	21.
Chair Backpack Table	22.	23.	24.

Writing Sentences with School Vocabulary

*Write   15   sentences using this chart. Take one line from each column to form a sentence.

Example: **My brother needs a marker. I need a pencil. She needs a ruler.**

I need	a pencil.
You need	a pen.
He needs	a marker.
She needs	some paper.
We need	a sheet of paper.
They need	an eraser.
	a book.
Mary needs	a ruler.
My sister needs	a pair of scissors.
My brother needs	some glue.
David needs	some paint.
Mary and David need	a paint brush.
Mary and Sue need	some crayons.
David and Bob need	a paper clip.
Mary and I need	some tape.
Bob and I need	a stapler.
	a spiral notebook.
	a pencil sharpener.

1._____

2._____

3._____

4._____

5._____

6._____

7._____

8._____

9._____

10._____
11._____
12._____
13._____
14._____
15._____

*Write 15 questions using this chart.

May I please borrow	a pencil?
	a pen?
	an eraser?
	some paper?
	a sheet of paper?
	a paper clip?
	a marker?
	some glue?
	a pair of scissors?
	a ruler?
	some crayons?
	a pencil sharpener?
	some paint?
	some tape?
	a stapler?

Example: May I please borrow a pencil?

1._____
2._____
3._____
4._____
5._____

6. _____

7. _____

8. _____

9. _____

10. _____

11. _____

12. _____

13. _____

14. _____

15. _____

* When you finish, find someone who is finished writing, too. Read your sentences and questions to each other.

Dialogues: Borrowing School Items

Dialogues #1, #2: Borrowing – **Partner Practice**

- *Students in the class pair up.*
- *Students put their own school supplies on top of their desks.*
- *They will practice Dialogues #1 and #2 with each other using their school supplies.*

Dialogue #1

Student A: "May I please borrow ___ _____?"
Student B: "Yes, here."
Student A: "Thank you."
Student B: "You're welcome."

Dialogue #2

Student A: "I need ___ _____."
Student B: "Here."
Student A: "Thank you."
Student B: "You're welcome."

Prepositions

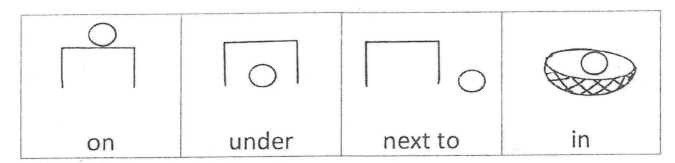

| on | under | next to | in |

#1 Speaking

*Your teacher will demonstrate these prepositions by using this dialogue and moving the ball to several locations.

Teacher: " Where is the ball?"

Class: "The ball is on the table."

#2 Writing

1.	*The ball is in the basket.*
2.	
3.	
4.	

*Match the sentences to the pictures.

The ball is on the table.   The ball is next to the table.

The ball is under the table.   The ball is in the basket.

Use the Prepositions to Talk about School Supplies

5.	*The glue is next to the scissors.*
6.	
7.	
8.	
9.	
10.	
11.	
12.	
13.	

*Match the sentences to the pictures:

The crayons are in the box.	The backpack is on the floor.	The pencil is in the pencil sharpener.
The stapler is on the table.	The pen is on the paper.	The paint brush is next to the paint.
The glue is next to the scissors.	The eraser is next to the paper.	The marker is under the ruler.

I Can't Find It

*Write 5 questions using this chart.

Where is	my pencil? my eraser? my black marker? my book? my ruler? my notebook? my pencil sharpener? my book bag?

Example: Where is my pencil?

1._____
2._____
3._____
4._____
5._____

*Write 5 questions using this chart.

Where are	my scissors? my markers? my colored pencils? my paper clips? my books? my crayons?

Example: Where are my scissors?

1._____
2._____

3._____
4._____
5._____

*Write 7 sentences using this chart.

Your pencil is	in Tom's book. on Tom's desk. under Tom's desk. under Tom's binder. on Tom's paper. in Tom's pencil pouch. on the floor. next to the trash can. in the pencil sharpener. next to the stapler.

Example: Your pencil is on Tom's desk.

1._____
2._____
3._____
4._____
5._____
6._____
7._____

Help Me Find My Pencil

Activity

Mary gives Bill her pencil and walks out of the room.	Bill hides Mary's pencil.	Mary comes back in and asks the class for help and they help her.

Mary Asks the Class for Help

Mary: **"Where is my pencil?"**

Class: Students raise their hands and Mary calls on different students to help her.

Mary: **"Susan, where is my pencil?"**

Susan: **"Your pencil is on the desk."**   (Example of possible answers.)

"Your pencil is in the book."

"Your pencil is in Bob's book."

*Several students take turns being Bill and Mary. Any object can be used for hiding.

Lesson # 6

Common Verbs

List of Verbs

Brush	Read
Buy	Run
Clean	Sing
Cook	Sleep
Dance	Study
Do	Take
Drink	Talk
Eat	Visit
Fix	Walk
Go	Wash
Listen	Watch
Make	Write
Paint	
Play	

15 Common Verbs

Label the Verbs

1.	2.	3.
4.	5.	6.
7.	8.	9.
10.	11.	12.
13.	14.	15.

Word Bank

buy	dance			sing	walk
clean	drink	listen	read	sleep	wash
cook	eat	play	run	walk	watch TV

Writing the "ing" Form of the Verb

Write the "ing" form of the verb next to the verb.

1. Play_____Playing_____
2. Walk_____
3. Wash_____
4. Watch_____
5. Clean_____
6. Cook_____
7. Listen_____
8. Eat_____
9. Drink_____
10. Buy_____
11. Sleep_____
12. Sing_____
13. Read_____
14. Run_____
15. Dance_____
16. Play_____

Eating
Singing
Sleeping
Buying
Drinking
Walking
Playing
Reading
Watching
Cooking
Cleaning
Washing
Running
Dancing
Listening

* Write the "ing" form of the verb in the sentence.

1. I am _____playing_____ baseball.   (play)
2. He is _____breakfast.   (eat)
3. They are _____in a contest.   (dance)
4. She is _____her clothes.   (wash)
5. Joe is _____with Mary.   (dance)
6. The baby is _____in a crib.   (sleep)
7. The children are _____ their favorite cartoons.   (watch)

8. They are _____ to Nick's new song.　(listen)

9. Linda is _____ to school.　(run)

10. Mrs. Anderson is _____ her room.　(clean)

11. Tommy is _____ lunch in the cafeteria.　(eat)

12. Mr. and Mrs. Bell are _____ cards with their friends.　(play)

13. The children are _____ a holiday song.　(sing)

14. They are _____ at a party.　(dance)

15. James is _____ a scary story.　(read)

16. My father is _____ the news on TV.　(watch)

17. Mrs. Worth is _____ groceries at the store.　(buy)

18. My aunt is _____ for the party.　(cook)

19. He is _____ after his dog.　(run)

20. Mike is _____ to school.　(walk)

21. The Lee family is _____ the house next to us.　(buy)

22. The kitten is _____ on the sofa.　(sleep)

23. Bob is _____ his new red car.　(wash)

24. Steve is _____ a cheese sandwich.　(eat)

25. The puppy is _____ water.　(drink)

*Write your own sentences with these verbs: **playing, drinking, running, watching, listening, washing, reading, sleeping, buying, eating***

26. _____

27. _____

28. _____

29. _____

30. _____

31. _____

32. _____

33. _____

34. _____

35. _____

Writing Sentences With the 15 Verbs

Write 15 sentences using this chart. Take the words from each column to make the sentence.

I am You are He is She is It is We are They are	singing. playing basketball. reading. listening to music. watching TV. dancing. drinking water. cooking. cleaning the kitchen. sleeping. eating dinner. walking to school. running around the track. buying an ice cream cone.

1. _____ *I am singing* _____ .

2. _____ .

3. _____ .

4. _____ .

5. _____ .

6. _____ .

7. _____ .

Writing Sentences With the 15 Verbs (continued)

8. _____.

9. _____.

10. _____.

11. _____.

12. _____.

13. _____.

14. _____.

15. _____.

16. _____.

Do you think you can write extra sentences?

_____.

_____.

_____.

_____.

_____.

Common Verbs:
What are they doing?

Look at the pictures to see what the people are doing.
Decide if the sentence should start with – He is, She is, They are.
Now, write a complete sentence to tell what they are doing.

1.	*He is reading.*
2.	
3.	
4.	

cooking	**Word Box**	playing	singing
cleaning	eating pizza	reading	walking
dancing	listening to music	running	watching TV

Common Verbs:
What are they doing?

5.	
6.	
7.	
8.	

	Word Box	
cooking		running
cleaning	listening to music	singing
dancing	playing	walking
eating pizza	reading	watching TV

Common Verbs:
What are they doing?

9.	
10.	
11.	

Word Box

cooking	listening to music	singing
cleaning	playing	walking
dancing	reading	watching TV
eating pizza	running	

15 Verbs: Answer the Questions

Example:

What am **I** doing?	*You are* eating.		
What are **you** doing?	*I am* eating.	What **is it** doing?	*It is* eating.
What is **he** doing?	*He is* eating.	What are **we** doing?	*We are* eating.
What is she doing?	*She is* eating.	What are **they** doing?	*They are* eating.

***Answer the questions in complete sentences:**

1. What are **you** doing?   (playing soccer)
    I am playing soccer.

2. What is **she** doing?   (washing clothes)

3. What is **he** doing?   (watching TV)

4. What is **it** doing?   (drinking water)

5. What are **they** doing?   (dancing)

6. What are **you** doing?   (doing my homework)

7. What are **we** doing?   (studying English)

8. What am I doing?   (writing sentences)

9. What is **brother** doing?   (playing football)

15 Verbs: Answer the Questions (continued)

10. What are **Mom and Dad** doing?   (reading the newspaper)

11. What are **you** doing?   (cleaning my room)

12. What is **Mary** doing?   (making dinner)

13. What is **Joe** doing?   (singing and playing the guitar)

14. What is the **dog** doing?   (sleeping)

15. What is **Grandmother** doing?   (listening to music)

16. What is **Grandfather** doing?   (drinking coffee)

17. What am **I** doing?   (working)

18. What are **you** doing?   (talking on the phone)

19. What are **they** doing?   (walking to school)

20. What are **they** doing?   (cleaning the house)

21. What is sister doing?   (exercising)

More Verbs

Write the verbs in your language.

1. write	2. brush	3. study
4. talk	5. go	6. work
7. paint	8. take	9. visit
10. make	11. do	12. fix

6-9:

Write the verb next to the "ing" form of the verb.

1. ___write___ writing	11. _____ walking
2. _____ brushing	12. _____ running
3. _____ studying	13. _____ playing
4. _____ talking	14. _____ dancing
5. _____ going	15. _____ washing
6. _____ working	16. _____ cleaning
7. _____ painting	17. _____ cooking
8. _____ taking	18. _____ listening
9. _____ visiting	19. _____ watching
10. _____ making	20. _____ drinking

Write Sentences With the New Verbs

I *am* eating.	It *is* eating.
You *are* eating.	You *are* eating. (plural)
He *is* eating.	We *are* eating.
She *is* eating.	They *are* eating.

Take words from each column and write at least 11 sentences. * *Be sure to use* **"am, are, is"** *correctly.*

	*	
I You He She It We They Joe Mary My mother My father My sister My friend My dog I	*am *are *is	cleaning the house. watching TV. talking on the phone. writing a letter. brushing the little girl's hair. going on a trip. working. painting the fence. taking a shower. making a cake. doing homework. fixing the car. playing ball. eating a sandwich. drinking water. sleeping.

Example:
I **am** *going on a trip.*
They **are** *going on a trip.*
My sister **is** *going on a trip.*

1._____.

Write Sentences With the New Verbs (continued)

2. _____.

3. _____.

4. _____.

5. _____.

6. _____.

7. _____.

8. _____.

9. _____.

10._____.

11._____.

_____.

_____.

_____.

_____.

_____.

_____.

More Verbs: Sentences

Write a complete sentence to answer the question.

1. What is **he** doing?

   He is running.

2. What is **she** doing?

   _____ _____talking on the phone.

3. What is **he** doing?

   _____ _____singing.

4. What are **they** doing?

   _____ _____going to the store.

5. What is **he** doing?

   _____ _____working.

6. What are **they** doing?

   _____ _____painting the house.

7. What is **he** doing?

   _____ _____taking a shower.

8. What is **she** doing?

   _____ _____brushing her hair.

9. What are **they** doing?

   _____ _____visiting Grandmother.

10. What is **she** doing?

    _____ _____making a cake.

Lesson #7

The Present Continuous

Affirmative

Negative

Questions

Overview of the Present Continuous

The Present Continuous – Happening Now

1. Use the present continuous when you want to talk about something that is **happening now.** It is in progress at this moment.

2. **Affirmative:** To make an affirmative sentence, use a subject, a "to be" verb, and the "ing" form of the verb.

(Subject)	('to be' verb)	(___ing form of the verb)
I	am	sleeping.
You	are	sleeping.
He	is	sleeping.
She	is	sleeping.
It	is	sleeping.
We	are	sleeping.
You	are	sleeping.
They	are	sleeping.

3. **Negative:** To make a negative sentence, put "not" after the "to be" verb (am, are, is).

(S) + (V) + *not* + (___ing)

I	am	*not*	sleeping.
You	are	*not*	sleeping.
He	is	*not*	sleeping.
She	is	*not*	sleeping.
It	Is	*not*	sleeping.
We	are	*not*	sleeping.
They	are	*not*	sleeping.

4. **Questions:** To make a question, move the "to be" verb to the beginning of the sentence.

(V) + (S) + (___ing)

Am	I	sleeping?
Are	you	sleeping?
Is	he	sleeping?
Is	she	sleeping?
Is	it	sleeping?
Are	we	sleeping?
Are	you	sleeping?
Are	they	sleeping?

Spelling Rules: Verbs with "ing"

Add "ing"

Brush brushing
Buy buying
Call calling
Chew chewing
Clean cleaning
Cook cooking
Cry crying
Do doing
Drink drinking
Dust dusting
Eat eating
Fix fixing
Fold folding
Follow following
Go going
Hang hanging
Help helping
Jump jumping
Laugh laughing
Listen listening
Look looking
Paint painting
Plant planting
Play playing
Pick picking
Read reading
Sing singing
Sleep sleeping
Study studying
Sweep sweeping
Talk talking
Visit visiting
Wait waiting
Walk walking
Wash washing
Watch watching
Wax waxing
Wear wearing
Work working
Vacuum vacuuming

Verbs ending with "e":
Drop the "e" and add "ing"

Bake baking
Bite biting
Chase chasing
Come coming
Dance dancing
Drive driving
Give giving
Have having
Leave leaving
Live living
Make making
Practice practicing
Rake raking
Ride riding
Shave shaving
Skate skating
Smile smiling
Take taking
Write writing

Verbs ending in a short vowel and consonant:
Double the final consonant and add "ing"

Babysit babysitting
Cut cutting
Drop dropping
Get getting
Hit hitting
Hug hugging
Mop mopping
Plan planning
Put putting
Run running
Set setting
Shop shopping
Sit sitting
Slip slipping
Stop stopping
Win winning

Spelling Practice: Verbs

"ing"	infinitive	Your language	"ing"	infinitive	Your language
babysitting	babysit		making		
baking			mopping		
biting			painting		
brushing			planning		
buying			planting		
calling			playing		
chasing			picking		
chewing			practicing		
cleaning			putting		
coming			raking		
cooking			reading		
crying			riding		
cutting			running		
dancing			setting		
doing			shaving		
drinking			singing		
driving			sitting		
dropping			skating		
dusting			sleeping		
eating			slipping		
fixing			smiling		
folding			stopping		
following			studying		
getting			sweeping		
giving			taking		
going			talking		
hanging			visiting		
having			waiting		
helping			walking		
hitting			washing		
hugging			watching		
jumping			waxing		
laughing			wearing		
leaving			winning		
living			working		
listening			writing		
looking			vacuuming		

Verbs: More Spelling Practice

Verb	"ing"	verb	"ing"
bake	*baking*	call	*calling*
come		clean	
dance		cook	
drive		cry	
give		do	
have		drink	
live		eat	
make		fix	
ride		go	
smile		help	
take		laugh	
write		listen	
		look	
babysit	*babysitting*	paint	
cut		plant	
drop		play	
get		read	
hit		sing	
hug		sleep	
mop		study	
plan		sweep	
put		talk	
run		visit	
shop		want	
sit		walk	
stop		wash	
		watch	
brush	*brushing*	work	

Practicing the Present Continuous

Explanation for the Affirmative

*The **Present Continuous** is used when you want to talk about what is happening **now**. It is in progress.*
It is formed like this:

(S) +	(V) +	(___ing)
I	am	cooking.
You	are	cooking.
He	is	cooking.
She	is	cooking.
It	is	cooking.
We	are	cooking.
They	are	cooking.

Affirmative

7-3 (a):   Present Continuous – Affirmative: **(S) + (V) + (___ing)**

*Write – **am, are, is** – in the blanks.*

1. We____*are*_____ working in the yard.
2. I _____planting flowers.
3. My father _____mowing the lawn.
4. My father _____cutting the grass.
5. My brother _____raking the leaves.
6. We _____cleaning the kitchen.

7. They _____washing the dishes.
8. Tom _____drying the dishes.
9. Sue _____putting away the dishes.
10. Bill _____taking out the trash.
11. You _____sweeping the floor.
12. I _____mopping the floor.

Present Continuous – Affirmative (continued)

7-3 (b): (S) + (V) + (____ing)

Write the 'ing' form of the verb in the blanks.

1. We are _____*doing*_____ the laundry. *(do)*

2. You are _____ the living room. (clean)

3. We are _____ our clothes. (wash)

4. They are _____ you. (help)

5. Jan is _____ up the shirts. (hang)

6. Pam is _____ the furniture. (dust)

7. Frank is _____ the towels. (fold)

8. The twins are _____ the floor. (wax)

9. The twins are _____ their bedroom. (clean)

10. Don is _____ the carpet. (vacuum)

11. Ben is _____ up the bed. (make)

12. We are _____ hungry. (get)

13. Len is _____ up the toys. (pick)

14. I am _____ sandwiches. (make)

7-3 (c): ***Choose a partner.*** You read the 12 sentences in 7-3(a), and your partner reads the 14 sentences in 7-3(b). Then, you switch, and he/she reads the 12 sentences, and you read the 14 sentences.

Present Continuous – Affirmative

Quiz

7-3(d):

Write sentences in the present continuous. Follow the model.

1. (Mother - cook)   **Mother is cooking.**

2. (The baby - sleep)

3. (The twins - play)

4. (I - write)

5. (The baby - cry)

6. (You - study)

7. (Sam - sing)

8. (We - eat)

9. (I - babysit)

10. (They - paint)

11. (Dad - shave)

12. (Bob and Jane - dance)

13. (Mary - set the table)

14. (You and I - make dinner)

15. (Ben and Len - help us)

16. (Mr. Smith - fix the car)

17. (Grandfather and Grandmother - watch TV)

18. (It - chase a cat)

19. (You - do a good job)

20. (We - take a test)

21. (You - clean)

Grandfather and Grandmother are Coming to Visit!

The Parker family is very busy today. Grandfather and Grandmother are coming to visit! It is **Saturday morning.** Mr. Parker is mowing the lawn. Mrs. Parker is doing the laundry. Betty is changing the sheets and making up the beds. Frank is vacuuming the whole house. Annie is dusting all of the furniture. Tim is cleaning the bathrooms. Everyone is working hard!

It is **Saturday afternoon.** Everyone is still preparing for the visit. Frank is at the gas station. He is filling the car with gas. Tim is at the bank. He is getting money. Mrs. Parker is at the grocery store. She is buying food. Betty is at the bakery. She is buying a pretty cake and donuts. They are Grandfather's favorite snacks. Annie is at the florist. She is buying pink roses. They are Grandmother's favorite flowers. Mr. Parker is at the airport. He is waiting for Grandfather and Grandmother!

*Answer in **complete sentences.***

Saturday Morning:

1) What is Annie doing?
   Annie is dusting all of the furniture.

2) Who is mowing the lawn?

3) What is Frank doing?

4) What is Betty doing?

5) Who is cleaning the bathrooms?

6) What is Mrs. Parker doing?

Saturday Afternoon:

7) Who is buying a pretty cake and donuts?

8) Who likes pink roses?

9) Who is getting money?

10) Where is Frank and what is he doing?

11) Where is Mrs. Parker and what is she doing?

12) Who is waiting for Grandfather and Grandmother?

Writing on Your Own

It is cleaning day at **your** house. What chores are you doing? What chores are the other people doing? *Write at least 5 sentences telling us about what everybody is doing.*

_____

_____

_____

_____

_____

_____

_____

_____

_____

_____

The Present Continuous Negative

Explanation for the Negative

The Present Continuous Negative: The Negative is formed by putting **"not"** after the "to be" verb (**am, are, is**).

(S)	+	(V)	+	not	+	(_____ing)
I		am		*not*		eating.
You		are		*not*		eating.
He		is		*not*		eating.
She		is		*not*		eating.
It		is		*not*		eating.
We		are		*not*		eating.
They		are		*not*		eating.

7-4 (a): The Present Continuous – Negative: *Make these sentences negative by putting "not" after - am, are, is.*

1. The baby is crying.

    *The baby is **not** crying.*

2. The baby is sleeping.

3. The twins are playing video games.

4. Tom is taking a nap.

5. Sue is talking to her boyfriend.

6. We are making a mess.

7. They are getting married.

8. I am feeling tired.

9. You are listening to me.

10. The dog is making noise.

11. It is raining.

Writing Sentences in the Present Continuous Negative

7-4 (b): *Write 14 sentences using this chart.*

I am You are He is She is We are They are Mary is Bob is Len and Ben are	**not**	running in the hall. talking in class. yelling. bothering him. chewing gum in class. copying her work. making noise. playing in class. playing in the cafeteria.

Example: **I am not chewing gum in class.**

1. _I am **not** running in the hall_
2. _____
3. _____
4. _____
5. _____
6. _____
7. _____
8. _____
9. _____
10. _____
11. _____
12. _____
13. _____
14. _____
15. _____

*Choose a partner and read exercises 7-4(a) and 7-4(b) to each other.

Mrs. Smith is Scolding Them!

Tell Mrs. Smith you are **not** doing that!

Get a partner. One of you is Mrs. Smith. One of you is the student.

*Mrs. Smith **reads** the sentence. The student **changes the sentence to a negative** and says the **negative** sentence.*
(Take turns being Mrs. Smith. Follow the example.)

Mrs. Smith: *You are running in the hall!*

Student: *No, Mrs. Smith. I am not running in the hall.*

1. You are running in the cafeteria!
2. You are talking in class!
3. You are chewing gum in class!
4. You are copying her work!
5. You are fighting with your brother!
6. You are bothering him!
7. You are pushing her desk!
8. You are wasting time!

Mrs. Smith: She is running in the hall!

Student: *No, Mrs. Smith. She is not running in the hall.*

9. She is being noisy in the cafeteria!
10. They are making noise in the library!
11. They are running in the hall!
12. He is copying Mary's homework!
13. Tom is bothering Joe!
14. He is acting silly in math class!
15. She is passing notes in class!

Quiz
Present Continuous Negative

Make negative sentences. Follow the model.

1. I (cook)
   *I am **not** cooking.*

2. You (cook)
   *You are **not** cooking.*

3. He (cook)
   *He is **not** cooking.*

4. I (eat)

5. You (clean)

6. He (yell)

7. She (run)

8. It (rain)

9. We (cook)

10. They (copy)

11. Bob (talk)

12. Mary and Bob (play)

13. She (cry)

Questions in the Present Continuous

Explanation: Questions in the Present Continuous

Questions in the Present Continuous: Form Questions in the Present Continuous like this – (V) + (S) + ("ing" Verb)

("To Be" Verb = am, are, is) + (Subject = I, you, he, she, it, we, you, they) + (___ing form of the Verb)

(V) + (S) + (___ing)

Am	I	winning?
Are	you	winning?
Is	he	winning?
Is	she	winning?
Is	it	winning?
Are	we	winning?
Are	you	winning?
Are	they	winning?

7-5 (a): Questions:

*Change these sentences to **questions** by placing the "to be" verb (am, are, is) at the beginning of the sentence.*

1. She **is** talking to her mother.

      ***Is** she talking to her mother?*

2. She is talking to her father.

3. I am talking too loud.

4. He is doing his homework.

5. We are taking the test tomorrow.

6. It is raining outside.

7. The bus is on time.

8. We are having a party.

9. I am bringing the chips.

10. You are bringing the sodas.

11. They are bringing the food.

12. He is bringing the cups, plates, and napkins.

13. You are inviting all of our friends.

7-5 (b): questions (continued)

Fill in the subject and verb in the correct order.

1. _____ _____ **making breakfast?** **(she)**

   _**Is**_ _**she**_ *making breakfast?*

2. _____ _____ making dinner? (we)

3. _____ _____ cooking for everybody? (we)

4. _____ _____ setting the table? (she)

5. _____ _____ eating too much? (I)

6. _____ _____ cleaning the kitchen? (we)

7. _____ _____ washing the dishes? (he)

8. _____ _____ drying the dishes? (she)

9. _____ _____ putting away the dishes? (they)

10. _____ _____ doing the laundry? (you)

11. _____ _____ washing the clothes? (you)

12. _____ _____ folding the clothes? (she)

13. _____ _____ hanging up the shirts? (he)

14. _____ _____ putting away the clothes? (they)

7-5 (c): **Choose a partner and practice asking the questions with each other.**

7-5(d): **Write 8 questions on your own.**

1. _____ Is she cooking _____ ?
2. _____ ?
3. _____ ?
4. _____ ?
5. _____ ?
6. _____ ?
7. _____ ?
8. _____ ?
9. _____ ?

Yes/No - Short Answers

Explanation

The questions that we made can be answered with a "yes" or "no" short answer.

Question	Yes - short answer	No - short answer/ (with "not")	No - short answer (with "isn't/aren't")
Am I winning?	Yes, you are.	No, you're *not.*	No, you *aren't.*
Are you winning?	Yes, I am.	No, I'm *not.*	------------------
Is he winning?	Yes, he is.	No, he's *not.*	No, he *isn't.*
Is she winning?	Yes, she is.	No, she's *not.*	No, she *isn't.*
Is it winning?	Yes, it is.	No, it's *not.*	No, it *isn't.*
Are we winning?	Yes, we are.	No, we're *not.*	No, we *aren't.*
Are they winning?	Yes, they are.	No, they're *not.*	No, they *aren't.*

7-6 (a): Yes - short answers

Answer all the questions with a "Yes-short answer."

1. Are they driving us to the game?

   Yes, they are.

2. Are we playing at 2 o'clock?

3. Are we playing the red team?

4. Are you practicing for the game?

5. Are you wearing a new jersey?

6. Am I batting first?

7. Is he batting last?

8. Is she cheering for us?

9. Are they driving us home?

10. Is he driving the big van?

11. Are we stopping for hamburgers?

12. Is he paying for the hamburgers?

Yes/No   Short Answers (continued)

7-6 (b): "No- short answer" with "not":

*Answer all these questions with a **"No-short answer"** using **"not."**

1. Are you running in the hall?   *No, I'm not.*

2. Is she chewing gum in class?

3. Is it snowing outside?

4. Is he taking the bus to work?

5. Am I making too much noise?

6. Are we following directions?

7. Are they making a cake?

8. Are you playing chess?

9. Are you working tonight?

10. Is he going to New York?

11. Is she taking the bus?

7-6 (c): "No - short answer" with " isn't/aren't":

*Answer these questions with the "No-short answer" using " **isn't or aren't."**

1. Is he playing soccer?   *No, he isn't.*

2. Is he playing baseball?

3. Is she playing ping pong?

4. Is it snowing outside?

5. Are they painting the house?   *No, they aren't.*

6. Are they eating pizza?

7. Are we taking a vacation?

8. Am I driving well?

7-6(d):

*Choose a partner and **practice** the "Yes - short answers" and the "No - short answers."*

Using What We've Learned

*You are going to write 3 sentences for each example.

1) Question

2) No-short answer

3) Sentence on what they are really doing.

*Follow the examples.

1. *Is he studying? (watching TV)*
   - **Is he studying?**
   - **No, he isn't.**
   - **He is watching TV.**

2. * Are they playing football? (baseball)*
   - **Are they playing football?**
   - **No, they aren't.**
   - **They are playing baseball.**

3. *Is he playing basketball? (soccer)*

   _____?

   _____.

   _____.

4. *Is he writing a letter?   (song)*

   _____?

   _____.

   _____.

5. *Is she studying science?   (math)*

   _____?

   _____.

   _____.

Using What We've Learned (continued)

6. *Is he fixing his car?*   *(truck)*

_____?

_____.

_____.

7. *Is she washing her dresses?* *(jeans)*

_____?

_____.

_____.

8. *Are they painting the house?* *(garage)*

_____?

_____.

_____.

9. *Are we making a cake?*   *(pie)*

_____?

_____.

_____.

10. *Are we taking the train?*   *(bus)*

_____?

_____.

_____.

11. *Are we playing the blue team?* *(red team)*

_____?

_____.

_____.

12. *Are they visiting their grandparents?* *(cousins)*

_____?

_____.

_____.

Using What We've Learned (continued)

13. *Are they eating fish? (chicken)*

_____?

_____.

_____.

14. *Is she reading a scary story? (love story)*

_____?

_____.

_____.

15. *Is Mrs. Jones drinking tea? (coffee)*

_____?

_____.

_____.

16. *Is Mary talking to her counselor? (teacher)*

_____?

_____.

_____.

17. *Is the dog running after the squirrel? (cat)*

_____?

_____.

_____.

18. *Am I running to the store? (playground)*

_____?

_____.

_____.

My Annoying Little Sister

My little sister is so annoying! She loves to play guessing games, especially on the phone! This is an example of our last conversation.

Me: Hi, little sister. May I please talk to Mom?

Little Sister: No, Mommy is busy.

Me: What is she doing?

Little Sister: Guess.

Me: Is she cleaning?

Little Sister: No, she isn't.

Me: Is she watching her favorite TV show?

Little Sister: No, she isn't.

Me: Is she taking a shower?

Little Sister: No, she isn't.

Me: Is she washing the dishes?

Little Sister: No, she isn't.

Me: Is she doing the laundry?

Little Sister: No, she isn't.

Me: Is she taking a nap?

Little Sister: No, she isn't.

Me: I give up! Tell me. What is Mom doing?

Little Sister: She is making dinner.

Me: Thank you, little sister. Tell Mom to call me when she gets a chance. Bye.

Little Sister: Okay, I'll tell her. Bye.

7-8 (a): ***Choose a partner and role play.***

7-8 (b): **Write about something that your little sister does to annoy you.**

_____

_____

_____

_____

_____

_____

_____

_____

Quiz on the Present Continuous

Affirmative

Negative

Questions

(A) Affirmative: *Write 11 sentences in the Present Continuous.*
1. I - clean
   I am cleaning.

2. You - clean
   You are cleaning.

3. She - clean
   She is cleaning.

4. He - run
5. It - rain
6. We - work
7. They - cook
8. You - study
9. I - babysit
10. You - paint
11. Dad - shave
12. Mom - sleep
13. My grandparents - read
14. The baby - cry

Quiz

(B) Negative: *Change these sentences to the negative.*

1. The baby is sleeping.
   The baby is <u>not</u> sleeping.

2. I am making noise.

3. You are running in the hall.

4. He is making a mess.

5. She is talking too much.

6. It is raining.

7. We are losing the game.

8. They are playing in class.

9. The machine is working.

10. The bus is running on time.

11. Jan is following directions.

12. The twins are cleaning their room.

13. Bob is mowing the lawn.

14. Meg is washing dishes.

15. The baby is taking a nap.

Quiz

(C) Questions: *Change these sentences to questions.*

1. She is going to the party.

   Is she going to the party?

2. He is taking a nap.

3. They are going on a trip.

4 . We are winning the game.

5. I am driving you home.

6. You are working this weekend.

7. He is buying a new bicycle.

8. She is visiting her grandmother.

9. It is raining outside.

10. We are doing it correctly.

11. They are getting married.

(D)Short Answers:

Answer the questions with a "Yes or No" short answer as it applies to you.

1. Are you a teenager?
2. Are you an adult?
3. Are you a child?
4. Are you in school?
5. Is this book difficult?
6. Is this book easy?
7. Is your friend fun to be with?
8. Is your friend nice?
9. Is your father tall?

Books may be ordered through Amazon.

About Chris Balli

- Master's in Education in Curriculum and Instruction with a concentration in TESOL University of Maryland, College Park

- 25 years of experience as an ESOL teacher in the public schools of Maryland and Connecticut

- 21 years of experience as an ESOL middle school teacher and 4 years as an elementary school and Adult Education teacher

- 25 years of experience with students who had gaps in their education or who were illiterate

- 25 years of writing curriculum to meet the needs of these students

Coming Soon!

English Language Learning with Super Support:
A WORKBOOK for ESL / ESOL / EFL /ELL Students
Beginners – **Book 2**
- Sports and Recreation
- Health
- Simple Present Tense

English Language Learning with Super Support:
A WORKBOOK for ESL / ESOL /EFL / ELL Students
Beginners – **Book 3**

- Regular Past Tense
- Irregular Past Tense
- Future

Questions? Comments? Contact the author at sscballi@gmail.com.

Made in the USA
Columbia, SC
19 February 2019